Its' A Boy

It's A Boy

Edited by Linda Sunshine
Designed by Barbara Scott-Goodman

Macmillan Publishing Company
New York

Maxwell Macmillan Canada
Toronto

Maxwell Macmillan International
New York   Oxford   Singapore   Sydney

Macmillan Publishing Company
866 Third Avenue
New York, NY 10022

Maxwell Macmillan Canada, Inc.
1200 Eglinton Avenue East, Suite 200
Don Mills, Ontario M3C 3N1

Macmillan Publishing Company is part of the Maxwell Communication Group of Companies.

Library of Congress Cataloging-in-Publication Data
It's a boy / edited by Linda Sunshine.
    p.   cm.
Summary: An illustrated anthology of excerpts from classic children's stories, poems, songs, nursery rhymes, and novels by authors like Byron, Saki, Yeats, Lewis Carroll, and Edith Wharton.
ISBN 0-02-615402-1
1. Boys—Literary collections.   [1. Boys—Literary collections.]   1. Sunshine, Linda.
PZ5.I84   1991   91-12712
820.8′092826—dc20   CIP
                                                                                                AC

Produced by Smallwood and Stewart, Inc., New York City

Macmillan books are available at special discounts for bulk purchases for sales promotions, premiums, fund-raising, or educational use. For details, contact: Special Sales Director, Macmillan Publishing Company, 866 Third Avenue, New York, NY 10022

10   9   8   7   6   5   4   3   2   1
Printed in Singapore

INTRODUCTION

*H*e was the most beautiful Prince that was ever born," begins a Victorian fairy tale, like an echo of what every parent must feel upon their birth of their own son.

Many artists, writers, and poets have attempted to describe the feeling of welcoming a newborn into the world. Marilyn French, for example, once said the emotion was ". . . somehow absolute, truer and more binding than any other experience life had to offer."

A child enters the world and the world is changed. And so this book celebrates the birth of your son, a magical creature. "A baby is God's opinion that the world should go on," wrote Carl Sandburg. And the world is surely a better place now that your son has arrived.

Linda Sunshine

To begin my life
with the beginning of my life,
I record that I was born
(as I have been informed and believe)
on . . .

Charles Dickens
David Copperfield

His Birthday . . . .

His Name . . . .

His Parents . . . .

His Birthplace . . . .

His Weight . . . .

His Measurement . . . .

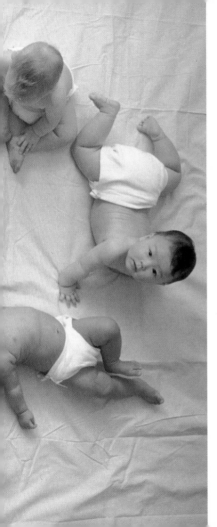

*E*very baby
born into the
world is a finer one
than the last.

Charles Dickens

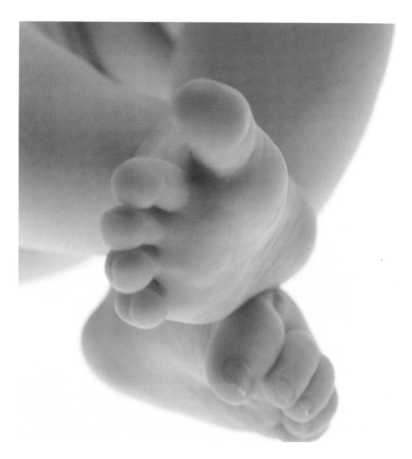

The child's foot still

doesn't know it's a foot,

it wants to be a butterfly or apple.

Pablo Neruda
To the Foot From Its Child

I was born in the year 1632, in the city of York, of a good family. . . . I was called Robinson Kreutznaer, but by the usual corruption of words in England, we are now called, nay, we now call ourselves and write our name, Crusoe, and so my companions called me.

Being the third son of the family and not bred to any trade, my head began to be filled very early with rambling thoughts. I would be satisfied with nothing but going to sea . . .

Daniel Defoe
Robinson Crusoe

YES, he was the most beautiful Prince that ever was born.

Of course, being a prince, people said this; but it was true besides. When he looked at the candle, his eyes had an expression of earnest inquiry quite startling in a newborn baby. His nose—there was not much of it certainly, but what there was seemed an aquiline shape. His complexion was a charming, healthy purple. He was round and fat, straight-limbed and long,—in fact, a splendid baby. Everybody was exceedingly proud of him, especially his mother and father, the King and Queen of Nomansland, who had waited for him during their happy reign of ten years—now made happier than ever, to themselves and their subjects, by the appearance of a son and heir.

Dinah Maria Mulock Craik
The Little Lame Prince and his Travelling-Cloak

Georgie Porgie,
puddin' and pie,
Kissed the girls
and made them cry.

When the boys
came out to play,
Georgie Porgie
ran away.

My mother loved children—
she would have given anything if I had been one.

Groucho Marx

*S*he took refuge in her newborn son ...
In her loneliness in the palace she learned
to know him, they learned to know each
other, and she discovered with great delight that
one does not love one's children just because they
are one's children but because of the friendship
formed while raising them.

Gabriel García Márquez
Love in the Time of Cholera

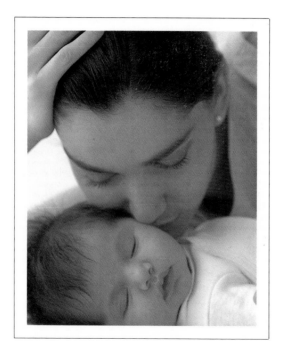

*S*oap and education are not as
sudden as a massacre, but they
are more deadly in the long run.

Mark Twain
The Facts Concerning the Recent Resignation

$\mathscr{H}$is little son into his bosom creeps,

The lively picture of his father's face.

Phineas Fletcher

*E*very father expects his boy
to do the things he wouldn't do
when he was young.

Kin Hubbard

I'm nobody! Who are you?
Are you nobody, too?
Then there's a pair of us—don't tell!
They'd banish us, you know.

How dreary to be somebody!
How public, like a frog
To tell your name the livelong day
To an admiring bog!

Emily Dickinson
I'm Nobody! Who Are You?

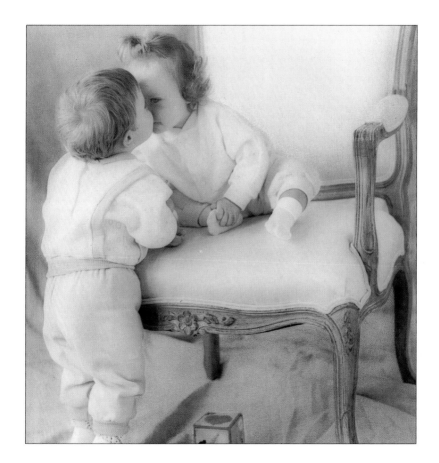

How his mother nursed him, and dressed him, and lived upon him; how she drove away all nurses, and would scarce allow any hand but her own to touch him. . . . This child was her being. Her existence was a maternal caress. She enveloped the feeble and unconscious creature with love and worship. It was her life which the baby drank from her bosom. Of night, and when alone, she had stealthy and intense raptures of motherly love, such as God's marvellous care has awarded to the female instinct—joys how far higher and lower than reason—blind beautiful devotions which only women's hearts know.

William Makepeace Thackeray
Vanity Fair

There never was a child so lovely
but his mother was glad to get him asleep.

Ralph Waldo Emerson
Journals of Ralph Waldo Emerson

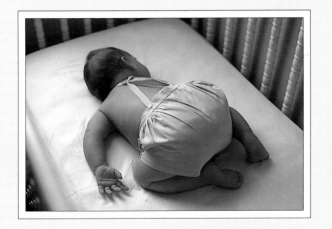

*W*hen the first baby laughed for the first time,

the laugh broke into a thousand pieces

and they all went skipping about,

and that was the beginning of fairies.

J.M. Barrie

cs

*S*ons are the anchors
of a mother's life.

Sophocles
Phaedra

cs

When his first-born was put into his arms, he could see that the boy had inherited his own eyes, as they once were—large, brilliant, and black. On that occasion, he again, with a full heart, acknowledged that God had tempered judgement with mercy.

Charlotte Brontë
Jane Eyre

A fairly bright boy is far more intelligent and far better company than the average adult.

J.B.S. Haldane

*W*hen you are dealing with a child, keep all your wits about you, and sit on the floor.

Austin O'Malley
Keystones of Thought

THERE AREN'T THAT MANY COWBOYS THESE DAYS, not real ones like Pecos Bill. Bill was a piece of work, all right. He was the dog-gonedest, gol-dingedest, dad-blamedest son of the prairie sod who ever rode across these here United States. Any cow puncher worth a lick will tell you that if it weren't for Bill, there wouldn't have been a Wild West. It would have been plain old mundane.

It took a man like Pecos Bill to conquer the West. Before he came on the scene cowboys didn't know a thing about cows. And let me tell you, a cowboy who doesn't know about cows is pretty lame. But we're putting our socks on over our boots here, sliding down the hill before we know where the cactus are, getting a little bit ahead of ourselves. Because to understand what Bill was about, you've got to know he was half coyote.

Brian Gleeson
Pecos Bill

*M*y boy ... always try to rub up
against money, for if you rub up
against money long enough, some of it
may rub off on you.

Damon Runyon
Furthermore

When I was a boy, I dreamed that I sat always at the wheel of a magnificent Stutz—in those days the Stutz was the stamp of the romantic life—a Stutz as low as a snake and as red as an Indiana barn.

F. Scott Fitzgerald
The Crack-Up

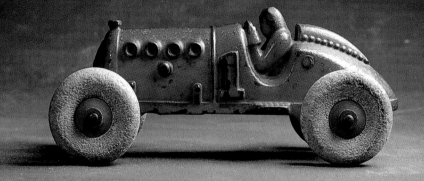

IT'S A BOY

You are a human boy, my young friend.

A human boy.

O glorious to be a human boy! . . .

O running stream of sparkling joy

To be a soaring human boy!

Charles Dickens
Bleak House

I do not know what I may appear to the world; but to myself I seem to have been only like a boy playing on the seashore, and diverting myself in now and then finding a smoother pebble or a prettier shell than ordinary, whilst the great ocean of truth lay all undiscovered before me.

Sir Isaac Newton
Brewster, Memoirs of Newton

That great cathedral space

which was childhood.

Virginia Woolf

Yours is the Earth

and everything that's in it,

And—which is more—

you'll be a Man, my son!

Rudyard Kipling
Rewards and Fairies

*M*rs. Banks was patting her children gently, first one and then the other, and murmuring words that were meant to be reassuring. Suddenly John stopped crying. He had very good manners, and he was fond of his Mother and remembered what was due to her. It was not *her* fault, poor woman, that she always said the wrong thing. It was just, he reflected, that she did not understand. So, to show that he forgave her, he turned over on his back, and very dolefully, sniffing back his tears, he picked up his right foot in both hands and ran his toes along his open mouth.

"Clever One, oh, Clever One," said his Mother admiringly. He did it again and she was very pleased.

P.L. Travers
Mary Poppins

When I am grown to man's estate
I shall be very proud and great
And tell the other girls and boys
Not to meddle with my toys.

Robert Louis Stevenson
Looking Forward

*T*he children never doubt that the great old trees in whose shade they play will stand forever, that one day they will grow to be strong like their fathers, fertile like their mothers, that they will live and prosper and raise their own children and grow old in the place where they were born. What has made it impossible for us to live in time like fish in water, like birds in air, like children?

J.M. Coetzee
Waiting For The Barbarians

*M*y lovely living boy,

My hope, my hap,

my love, my life,

my joy.

Guillaume de Salluste, Seigneur Du Bartas
Fourth Day

At seven, when I go to bed,
I find such pictures in my head:
Castles with dragons prowling around,
Gardens where magic fruits are found;
Fair ladies prisoned in a tower,
Or lost in an enchanted bower;
While gallant horsemen ride by streams
That border all this land of dreams
I find, so clearly in my head
At seven, when I go to bed.

Robert Louis Stevenson
A Child's Thought

A boy is a magical creature —

you can lock him out of your workshop,

but you can't lock him out of your heart.

Allan Beck

I am convinced that every boy,

in his heart, would rather steal

second base than an automobile.

Thomas Campbell Clark

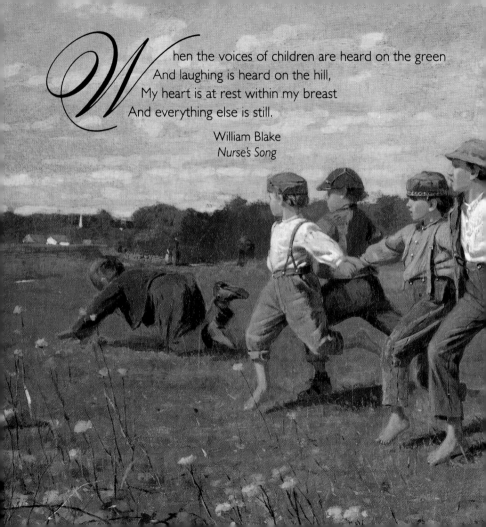

When the voices of children are heard on the green
And laughing is heard on the hill,
My heart is at rest within my breast
And everything else is still.

William Blake
Nurse's Song

I meant to do my work to-day—
But a brown bird sang in the appletree,
And a butterfly flitted across the field,
And all the leaves were calling me.

And the wind went sighing over the land,
Tossing the grasses to and fro,
And a rainbow held out its shining hand—
So what could I do but laugh and go?

Richard Le Gallienne
The Lonely Dancer

Ah!

happy years!
once more who would not be a boy?

Lord Byron
Childe Harold's Pilgrimage

All I can tell 'em is pick a good one and sock it. I get back to the dugout and they ask me what it was I hit and I tell 'em I don't know except it looked good.

Babe Ruth
The American Treasury

No game in the world is as tidy and dramatically neat as baseball, with cause and effect, crime and punishment, motive and result, so cleanly defined.

Paul Gallico
The Baseball Reader

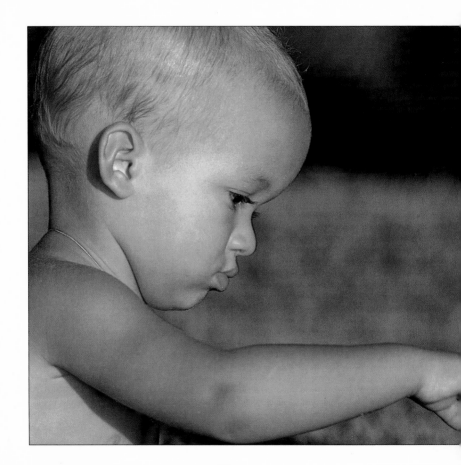

Two friends playing together.
And love is when you like to play
when he wants to and you may not want to.

David Wilson, age 7, United States
*Journeys: Words of Children
of the English-Speaking World*

O wonderful son, that can so astonish a mother!

William Shakespeare
Hamlet

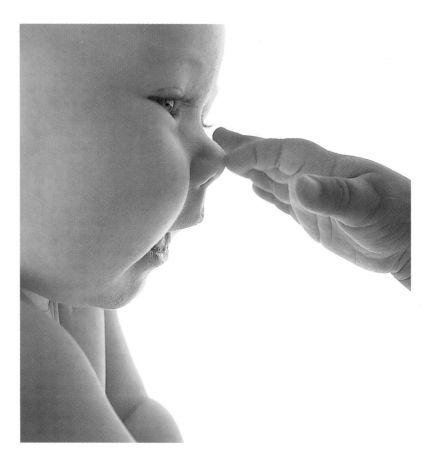

I wish that I could understand
The moving marvel of my Hand;
I watch my fingers turn and twist,
The supple bending of my wrist,
The dainty touch of my finger-tip,
The steel intensity of grip;
A tool of exquisite design,
With pride I think: "It's mine! It's mine!"

Robert W. Service
The Wonderer

As the little prince dropped off to sleep, I took him in my arms and set out walking once more. I felt deeply moved, and stirred. It seemed to me that I was carrying a very fragile treasure. It seemed to me, even, that there was nothing more fragile on all the Earth. In the moonlight I looked at his pale forehead, his closed eyes, his locks of hair that trembled in the wind, and I said to myself: "What I see here is nothing but a shell. What is more important is invisible . . ."

Antoine de Saint-Exupéry
The Little Prince

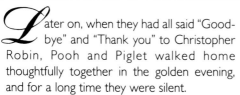

*L*ater on, when they had all said "Good-bye" and "Thank you" to Christopher Robin, Pooh and Piglet walked home thoughtfully together in the golden evening, and for a long time they were silent.

"When you wake up in the morning, Pooh," said Piglet at last, "what's the first thing you say to yourself?"

"What's for breakfast?" said Pooh. "What do you say, Piglet?"

"I say, I wonder what's going to happen excit-ing *today*?" said Piglet.

Pooh nodded thoughtfully. "It's the same thing," he said.

A.A. Milne
Winnie-the-Pooh

A baby is God's opinion that the world should go on.

Carl Sandburg

❦

The child is the father of the man.

❦

William Wordsworth

PERMISSIONS
AND PHOTO CREDITS

24: Photograph by Monica Roberts.

26-27: Photograph by Monica Roberts.

28: Photograph of Sebastian and Duncan White by Arthur Elgort.

31: Photograph by Katie Gray.

32: "Maternity" by Beatrice Howe. Reprinted with permission of The Bridgeman Art Library, Limited.

35: Photograph by Monica Roberts.

37: Photograph by Pheobe Dunn.

38-39: "The Monet Family in Their Garden" by Edouard Manet. Copyright © 1990 The Metropolitan Museum of Art, The Metropolitan Museum of Art, bequest of Joan Whitney Payson, 1975. (1976.201.14)

41: Photograph by Penny Gentieu.

42-43: Photograph by Marcia Lippman.

44: Excerpt from *Pecos Bill* by Brian Gleeson. Copyright © 1988 Rabbit Ears Productions. Reprinted by arrangement with Picture Book Studio.

45: Photograph by Alexandra Stonehill.

46: Photograph by Penny Gentieu.

49: Photograph by Ron Harris.

50: Photograph of Adam Dorenter by Susan Dorenter.

52-53: Photograph by John Lynch.

54: "In the Daisy Field" by Minnie Smythe. Reprinted with permission of The Bridgeman Art Library, Limited.

57: Photograph by Alexandra Stonehill.

58: Photograph by Penny Gentieu.

59: Excerpt from *Mary Poppins*, copyright 1934 and renewed 1962 by P.L. Travers, reprinted by permission of Harcourt Brace Jovanovich, Inc.

60: Photograph by Monica Roberts.

62: Photograph of Duncan White by Arthur Elgort.

63: *Waiting For The Barbarians* by J.M. Coetzee is reprinted by permission of Viking Penguin Publishers.

64: Photograph by D. Cavagnaro.

67: "The Two Brothers" by Honor Appleton. Reprinted by permission of The Bridgeman Art Library, Limited.

68-69: Photograph by Tina Mucci.

70: "Boy with Baseball" by George Benjamin Luks. Copyright © 1984 The

Metropolitan Museum of Art, The Metropolitan Museum of Art, Edward Joseph Gallagher III Memorial Collection, 1954. (54.10.2)

72-73: "Snap the Whip" by Winslow Homer. Copyright © 1984 The Metropolitan Museum of Art, The Metropolitan Museum of Art, Gift of Christian A. Zabriskie, 1950. (50.41)

74: Photograph by Kathryn Abbe.

77: Photograph of Zachary Ross White by Vinnie Fish.

78: Photograph courtesy of the National Baseball Library, Cooperstown, N.Y.

79: Photograph courtesy of the National Baseball Library, Cooperstown, N.Y.

80-81: Photograph by Jerry Simpson.

82: Photograph by Barbara Campbell.

84: Photograph by Penny Gentieu.

86: Excerpt from *The Little Prince* by Antoine de Saint-Exupery, copyright 1984 and renewed 1971 by Harcourt Brace Jovanovich, Inc., reprinted by permission of the publisher.

87: Photograph by Monica Roberts.

88-89: Excerpt from *Winnie-the-Pooh* by A. A. Milne. Copyright 1926 by E.P. Dutton, renewed 1954 by A. A. Milne. Used by permission of the publisher, Dutton Children's Books, a division of Penguin Books USA Inc. Photograph by Monica Roberts.

90: Photograph by Penny Gentieu.

92: Photograph by Monica Roberts.